MOM
AND
DEMENTIA
AND
ME

To: Sarah
Fm: Gene
Thanks for
for coming!

Secant Publishing, LLC
P.O. Box 4059
Salisbury MD 21803
www.secantpublishing.com

Publisher's Cataloging-in-Publication data

Names: Illig, Leona Upton, author.
Title: Mom and dementia and me: a caregiver's journey / by Leona
Upton Illig.
Description: Salisbury, MD: Secant Publishing, 2021.
Identifiers: LCCN: 2021921937 | ISBN: 978-0-9997503-8-4
(paperback) | 978-0-9997503-9-1 (ebook)
Subjects: LCSH Illig, Leona Upton. | Dementia--Patients--
United States--Family relationships. | Dementia--Patients-
-United States--Biography. | Dementia--Patients--Care. |
Caregivers--Biography. | Mothers and daughters--United States.
| BISAC BIOGRAPHY & AUTOBIOGRAPHY / Personal
Memoirs | FAMILY & RELATIONSHIPS / Life Stages /
Later Years | HEALTH & FITNESS / Diseases / Alzheimers &
Dementia | HEALTH & FITNESS / Health Care Issues
Classification: LCC RC521 .I45 2021 | DDC
362.196/83/092--dc23

Cover design by C.S. Fritz

MOM AND DEMENTIA AND ME

A Caregiver's Journey

LEONA UPTON ILLIG

For Mom

Vivian Elizabeth Upton

née McKenzie

TABLE OF CONTENTS

FOREWORD

This book is not about the devastation of dementia. There are enough of those around. Nor is it a lighthearted look at a disease that is responsible for about 250,000 deaths in the United States each year. What this book is, is this: a narrative of my experiences caring for Mom during the last years of her life, as she struggled with Lewy body dementia. It is written from a layperson's point of view in the hope that you, the reader, will be able to benefit from our experiences. I'm not a doctor, nurse, professional caregiver, physical therapist, emergency medical technician, or ... well, you get the idea. I'm probably someone just like you.

When Mom and I started this journey, we knew nothing about dementia in general, or Lewy body in particular. Yes, we had heard about Robin

Williams, but we immediately thought, *Well, that will never happen to us.* If that sounds like you and your family, read on.

By the time our journey was over, I had been educated. I had gotten help. But the fact is, I wish I had known more about this disease and its effects right from the start. I might have avoided a lot of stress on my family, on me . . . and on Mom.

Hence, this book. Not all dementias are alike, and my experience may not be like yours. Every situation is different, with a surprise lurking around every corner. But it doesn't matter. If only one sentence in this book helps just one person, that's good enough for me. "Mission accomplished," as they say. Or maybe they don't say. Times change.

I said a few paragraphs ago that this is not a funny book. But it does have humor in it (at least, I hope so). We humans need laughter. No matter how grim things get (and dementia can get very, very grim), you need to seek out smiles. It's no accident that only one letter separates grim from grin. And an "I" is in both of them. You can quote me on that.

The other reason that this book contains humor is because of Mom herself. Mom laughed, and her family laughed, too. She could be really funny, intentionally and accidentally. I couldn't write a book about Mom without some laughs sprinkled here and there.

And it's all true. Even the jokes. Despite the fact that dementia began to erode her mind and personality, she still had her moments. One Christmas, members of the church choir came to our house to sing carols. They were wonderful people, but while they were introducing themselves, Mom began to fidget. The carolers began to discuss which carols they might sing. Finally, after some deliberation, the minister looked at Mom and kindly asked her, "Mrs. Upton, what would you like us to sing?" Mom looked him straight in the eye and growled, "Just sing."

This book is for anyone who is struggling to help their parents, children, other relatives, friends, and colleagues with dementia. I tried to find a catch-all term for all these different categories of people to make the book easier to read. In the first draft I tried using the term, "loved one." But after the tenth iteration of "loved one," I began to feel like I was in a funeral home. So, I have used "Mom" throughout most of the book. But Mom could be anybody. It could even be you.

So, here's the book. It's meant to be easy to read and organized so that you can find things quickly. You don't have to read it straight through from beginning to end. We're not talking *Moby Dick* here. Look through the chapter headings, and if one describes the situation that you're facing now, start there if you want. Really, I won't mind. And there aren't any tests.

So. I just realized that I've written a memoir about forgetting. Pretty funny, eh?

And remember: just sing.

PART ONE

IN THE BEGINNING

"Now, Hal, what time of day is it, lad?"

FALSTAFF TO PRINCE HAL
Act 1, Scene 2
Henry IV, Part 1
By
William Shakespeare

CHAPTER ONE

THAT WILL NEVER, EVER, HAPPEN TO US

. . . Or Anybody Else We Know . . .

LET ME INTRODUCE YOU TO MOM. We'll call this part, "Intro to Mom 101."

Mom sailed into her eighties in good health. She had the usual ailments (high blood pressure, high cholesterol, and type 2 diabetes), but they were all controlled with medicines with the help of our family doctor. Except for a bout with breast cancer when she was sixty-six (it was successfully treated with a modified radical mastectomy and medicine), and problems with ingrown eyelashes, she had no serious health problems. She weighed about 110 pounds and had a good appetite, especially for oysters and hard crabs. We are serious Maryland seafood-eaters in our family.

Mentally and emotionally, we couldn't have asked for a better mom. We went shopping together, ate out together, and discussed the soap operas together (*As the World Turns* and *The Guiding Light* were our favorites). Mom, my younger sister, Barbara, and I went on trips together. Later, my husband, David, and I took Mom on vacations with us. She enjoyed visiting Williamsburg, Virginia; it was a magic place for us. The holidays were spent at either our house or hers.

Two deaths in our family hit us hard. The first was the death of my dad, Ridgely, from complications of heart problems, when Mom was 78. The second was the death of my sister, Barbara, from cancer, when Mom was 84.

These were terrible times. Mom, however, was strong. She was a survivor. She knew that life is a gift.

And she had an irrepressible sense of humor. For example: one afternoon Mom, Barbara, and I were watching television and the "dancing raisins commercial" came on. You know the one: a group of raisins comes dancing across the screen to the tune of, "I Heard it Through the Grapevine" by Marvin

Gaye. Mom had never seen the commercial before. She started laughing and couldn't stop, and from that time on, that commercial became part of our family folklore.

At this point you may be saying to yourself, "They seem to be watching a lot of television, don't they?" Yep, that's right! Mom watched a lot of television and enjoyed every minute of it. She also liked country music—the real singers, artists like Hank Williams and Patsy Cline. And polkas. Lawrence Welk was big at our house.

Did I mention that she was a farmer's wife? After Dad died, Mom lived on our small vegetable farm by herself. She had plenty of space and fresh air. For many years, there were dogs on the farm: beagles, and rumors of beagles. She owned her own car, although by the time she had reached her early eighties she wasn't driving much anymore. She loved her car, but she knew that her reflexes had dulled, and that it was better for her to stay off the road.

All this is by way of telling you: Mom, a sweet, strong person, lived pretty much a normal, happy life.

In 2014, Mom and I were shocked to hear that Robin Williams had died. We had loved *Mork & Mindy*. Neither of us had ever heard of his strange disease. In fact, we didn't know anything about dementia or Alzheimer's. Nobody we knew had those things. We were pretty confident, in fact, that those diseases only happened to other people.

How wrong we were.

CHAPTER TWO

WHAT JUST HAPPENED HERE?

And Please, Don't Let It Happen Again . . .

"COME ON, MOM!" We were shopping at the mall, and Mom was lagging behind. I had other errands to run after we finished, and I was impatient. "Can't you hurry up?" Mom was at least three steps behind me, and one footstep sounded much heavier than the other. *She must need new shoes*, I thought; we'll hit the shoe store on the next trip.

But we didn't buy new shoes because we didn't have a "next trip to the mall," at least not for a while. We were on the "down" escalator, literally, headed toward "women's cosmetics," when Mom suddenly sat down. On the moving escalator. Heading toward the point of no return, where the steps slide under the floor and you don't want to know what's underneath.

It's nice to think that when a crisis like this hits, and no one is around to help, one might have the presence of mind to take calm, immediate, and effective action.

Thus, you may not be surprised to learn that my first reaction was to say: "Mom, what are you doing down there?" To this day I do not know how I lifted Mom to her feet and got us off the escalator without calamity. As we stood in front of the cosmetics counter, Mom looked at me and nodded in satisfaction. "It's okay," she said. "Nobody saw me."

One thing to know about us is that the only important thing, in any family "incident," is if anybody *sees*. If no one sees it, it didn't happen.

Except, this time, I saw. And didn't understand. It was as if Mom's legs had temporarily weakened and could no longer carry her. Mom was in her mid-eighties. "Oh," I said to myself, "this is just old age; these things happen, and we have to learn to deal with them."

The next time Mom fell, it wasn't so easy to dismiss. She hurt her arm and thereby earned a trip to the ER. The doctor on duty recommended physical therapy and occupational therapy. We laughed when we heard that. Occupational therapy? Did they think, at age eighty-five, that Mom was going to start training as a welder? In reality, the therapists who were sent to Mom's house were terrific. They suggested ways of getting around the house safely, and exercises to increase arm and leg strength. We were lucky to have them (and Medicare and private insurance paid for them). We also learned the difference between physical and occupational therapy. The former focuses on increasing mobility, while the latter helps people live independently. Both helped. And we started to delude ourselves into thinking that Mom would bounce back from these setbacks.

But then the dizziness started. Mom had some brief dizzy spells when I was with her, and she told me about dizzy spells that she was having when she got out of bed. They seemed to come and go, without warning or pattern.

During one of these episodes, Mom fell in the bathroom. When the emergency medical technicians (EMTs) arrived, they recommended that we take her to the hospital to get her checked out. The doctor in the ER thought that she might be dehydrated, and she wound up staying in the hospital for a couple of days. Mom had always been a good patient at the doctor's office and in the hospital, but this time was different. She grew agitated. She thought that she was in her farmhouse, and that the nurses and doctors were people invading her home. I got a call at midnight from the nurses' station, asking me to come in to calm her down. I tried, but she didn't want to listen to me. This was not the Mom that I knew. One of the doctors prescribed an anti-psychotic drug. Mom had a bad reaction to it. When the drug wore off, Mom went to sleep. The next day, when the doctor came in, he said that she might have a form of dementia, and that she needed to see her primary care doctor for further evaluation.

This was the first time that we had ever heard the word "dementia" in connection with Mom's health. Our first reaction was, "That doctor is so wrong." But we made an appointment with her primary care doctor anyway. He would see us in three weeks.

At about this same time, Mom began doing strange things. She had always been diligent about going to the doctor for checkups, but now she didn't want any more mammograms, blood tests, or flu shots. "I'm too old for this," she told me. She began to misplace bills, money, and checkbooks, and her handwriting was becoming illegible. She was losing interest in her hobbies (mainly watching TV and picking up twigs and small tree branches that routinely fell in the yard). I went grocery shopping for her, normally about once a week. Suddenly she was asking for groceries two or three times a week—not a lot of groceries, but, unaccountably, the same groceries over and over again (to this day I'll never know what happened to all that food. When Mom moved out of her house, her refrigerator was nearly empty). One day she called me and, with great excitement, exclaimed, "Did you see where Dr. Silas has died?"

"Uh, no ..." I replied, and, trying to sound concerned, I said, "That's terrible." I hung up the phone and pondered who Dr. Silas was. It wasn't the name of any doctor that any of us had ever gone to. It was a little later that evening that I realized that Dr. Silas Clay was a fictional character on *General Hospital*. I wasn't watching the soaps at that time, and Mom knew that. Or, she used to know that.

Another weird occurrence happened when Mom fell in her bedroom one day. It was one of her "my legs couldn't hold me, and I just slid to the ground" episodes. She didn't hurt herself. And for a day or two afterwards she was her old self again: joking, cheerful, and completely rational. Then, just as quickly, she relapsed into her new, troubling behaviors. To this day we don't know how it happened, or why.

The last straw came when Mom called to say that she had gotten rid of the beehive in her bedroom. Bees were flying around the overhead ceiling light, she told me, so she had moved the bed, brought a step ladder inside, got up on it, and sprayed the bees with insecticide. They were all dead. "Everything's okay now," she told me, happy and full of confidence. A quick trip to her house revealed no step ladder, no insecticide, no hive . . . and no dead bees.

It finally dawned on me that Mom might have a serious health problem. And if you are saying to yourself, "You just figured that out now?", read on.

Chapter Three

"Denial Is Not
a River in Egypt"

— Comedians through the ages

It's easier than you might think to ignore the warning signs of a serious mental or physical illness. You don't want to admit that anything is wrong with Mom, because if there is an illness, there could also be . . . death. You don't want either of those. And if you allow for the possibilities that your mom might suffer, and that you might be left alone to face an unpleasant future . . . those aren't the outcomes that you want, either.

If your mom is elderly, society can make it easy for you to turn a blind eye to serious symptoms.

"It's only old age," you say to yourself. Or, "Wasn't Grandmom the same way?" Or, "These things happen to everyone at that age; it's just that in the old days we didn't talk about them or give them a name." Right.

Sometimes doctors, who are your lifeline when a serious illness strikes, aren't much help, at least at first. Most types of dementia can't be diagnosed until after death (I leave it up to you to decide whether this is good or bad). In the early stages of the disease, tests can be given to patients to diagnose dementia, but these tests are not one hundred percent accurate. In addition, dementia in the early stages can masquerade as other ailments, and your doctor might prescribe supplements for vitamin deficiencies, or more water to combat dehydration. If you are lucky, these prescriptions will help, and your mom will get better. That's the hope.

But . . . if the usual things don't seem to have any effect, you may not be dealing with the normal effects of aging. You may be looking at the early onset of one of the many different kinds of dementia.

Below are some of the early warning signs that I experienced with Mom. If you detect these symptoms in your mom, it doesn't necessarily mean that she has dementia. It does mean, however, that you should see a doctor and let her know what's happening.

The Early Warning Signs
That Mom Experienced:

1. Dizziness, especially when getting out of bed in the morning, or when getting up from the commode.

2. Weakness in limbs, especially in the legs; having trouble getting up or sitting down, particularly in big, soft-cushioned chairs.

3. Change in gait: the walking pace slows, and the feet don't seem to be working together as they should; instead, they seem to be shuffling. Your mom may appear to step heavily on one foot, and lightly on her other foot, almost as if one of her legs were shorter than the other. When walking with someone else, she always seems to be two steps behind.

4. A significant change in eating, characterized by either constant hunger or no appetite at all, and sometimes alternating between the two. Although your mom seems to be eating all the time, she doesn't gain any weight.

5. Confusing fictional events on TV shows with reality.

6. Talking about unusual, strange, or inappropriate subjects.

7. Delusions, confusion, or agitation.

8. Trying to hide physical and mental problems.

These were all warning signs that Mom had early dementia.

And I missed them all.

Chapter Four

Getting Your House in Order

"Homes are always one room short" (Leo Tolstoy)

DEMENTIA IS THE UNINVITED GUEST WHICH consumes everything in its path. You can't stop it. Your first reactions may be grief, fear, or helplessness. Even anger. But you can do some things right now to help yourself. Whether you think that your mom could be a candidate for dementia in the future, or you suspect that she already has it, you can take action. You don't need a doctor's appointment. Or a prescription.

When Mom began her journey into dementia, she looked at me and said, "Everything counts." I didn't know what she was referring to at the time, but she was right. No matter how small a step you take, or when you take it, it will help. Everything does count.

This chapter, and the one following it, contain ideas that may help you. They are based on my experiences with Mom. Take advantage of anything that you think you can use. I guess I should say that, if at all possible, the time to act is before dementia strikes. We all aspire to be prepared before the storm hits. But many of us aren't able to do that. If your mom is already deep into dementia, don't despair. It's never too late to take advantage of new equipment or techniques, or ideas that you might not have thought of before.

When you're standing at the edge of the cliff that is dementia, it's better to look down, not up. You know where you're headed, but you might see some ledges and branches that can break your fall or, at least, slow your descent. And that's a worthy goal.

Having said all that, the volume of advertising for personal equipment and new technologies seems to be growing faster than the population of senior citizens. Try to keep abreast of the latest developments via your health providers, senior centers, and social media. But from my experience, the most important thing, by far, is to get a bedroom and a bathroom, with a shower, set up on the first floor of your house. Probably nothing else you do will make your life, and the life of your mom, easier.

Naturally, Mom fought us on this. She had lived in a one-hundred-year-old farmhouse since she married Dad in 1949. She was satisfied with the house the way it was and didn't want to change anything. Upstairs (and the stairs were steep) were one small bathroom, no shower, and four bedrooms. On the ground floor were a large kitchen, a living room, and a dining room.

Mom was also vehemently opposed to a shower. "Never had one," she said. "Won't ever use one."

She had a point: trying to squeeze a bedroom and a bath into the ground floor would have been hard. Our solution was to build an addition onto the house: a bedroom with a new, modern bathroom, complete with a shower. Mom didn't like this idea either, but she went along with it. It turned out to be the best thing that we could have done; it allowed Mom to stay in her house years longer than she otherwise could have, and it made life easier for the various caregivers, and us, when we came over to help.

But not everyone has the time or the money to build an addition. You can still do other things, though. Do you have a dining room? Make it the new bedroom. Or take whatever space you have downstairs and make part of it into a bedroom. You can separate it with dividers or curtains, or anything you want to use. Then put a large, adult potty chair next to the bed. These chairs are sturdy without being too heavy to move around. They have good handrails, high seats, and their chamber pots or bowls are easy to remove from the framework. You can also buy disposable liners for the commode. Make sure that you put a trashcan close to the potty chair.

If there is no bathroom sink nearby, place a table, with some towels and containers that can hold water, close at hand. You can also purchase "dry" shampoos for your wash-up table. Put another table next to that with combs, brushes, and scissors. You might want to set up a separate table for medicines. All of these tables should be lightweight and easily moveable; card tables often work well. They are inexpensive, and you can find them in home remodeling stores or on the Internet.

Rearranging a house is no small thing. Just in itself, the process can cause stress. You can spend a lot of money on it, or you can spend little or nothing at all. You can opt for permanent construction or temporary changes.

But, once done, it will be worth its weight in gold.

CHAPTER FIVE

GADGETS AND GIZMOS

"Give us the tools" (Winston Churchill)

NOW TO SOME SMALLER, specific recommendations. Many tools of the trade don't require a major home makeover. Below are some of them. And remember, although it's best to acquire these tools before dementia takes over, you can start using them during any stage of the disease. It's never too late.

I know, lists are boring. But trust me, if I had had this list before Mom became sick, we would all have been much better prepared.

1. MEDICAL ALERT SYSTEM

There are lots of these around in the forms of necklaces, bracelets, smart watches, and smartphones, and they are widely advertised. They are useful if your mom gets into trouble (such as a fall) and needs help. But it's important to convince your mom to wear the alert system all the time. It won't help if your mom has fallen in the bathroom, and the medical alert necklace is on the nightstand. Look at the different options available, and pick the one that your mom will like (and use). My mom wore one of these medical alert systems around her neck, and I can testify, from our experience, that they work.

Some medical alert companies are expensive. Compare prices and check to see if your health insurance company will help pay for it. If cost is a problem, other resources are available. For example, there are services which will call your mom every day at a certain time to check to see that she is okay. They are often called "wellness calls" or "telephone reassurance programs" and are run by county and community agencies. Most of the time they are free. Check with your local Department of Aging.

2. LEGAL DOCUMENTS

You and your mom should establish a power of attorney for financial and legal matters, an advanced health directive, and a MOLST (Medical Orders for Life Sustaining Treatment) document. Your mom will also need a will. Make copies of everything. All of these forms should be put into folders and stored in places which are easily accessible to you, family members, and EMTs.

Let me emphasize that you should do this before an illness such as dementia strikes. Once dementia has set in, it can be hard to get your mom to understand the documents, much less sign them.

Another tip: many of these forms are available, for free, on the Internet. But, in my experience, it is better to have a lawyer draw them up for you. Laws change, different states have different regulations, and you need to know what your particular state requires. If cost is a problem, check with your state or county Department of Aging, or your local senior center. They probably have a list of lawyers who specialize in drawing up these documents and who are willing to help seniors at little or no cost. In fact, some lawyers regularly visit senior centers to help with such documents for free.

If your mom is too ill to help prepare or sign these documents, seek the advice of a lawyer. They will be able to help you.

3. BILLS

If you can, persuade your mom to have all her bills mailed to your house. Emphasize that she can still pay all the bills, but that you want to help her stay organized and up to date. Bills have a bad habit of continuing to arrive, whether or not the recipient is sick. The bills don't know, and they don't care. Important bills can get misplaced or lost in the urgency and confusion of illness. Sadly, this is a bigger deal than you might think, and change-of-address forms can take time to be processed. The sooner you get a handle on the bills, the better off you will be.

4. **LISTS OF IMPORTANT PEOPLE AND THINGS**
   Prepare four lists:
   1) a list of your mom's doctors;
   2) a list of medicines she's taking;
   3) a list of emergency contacts; and
   4) a list of your mom's daily activities.

   Sounds daunting, right? But don't be put off. Initially, it will take time to gather all this information, but after that, updating them will be a breeze.

   Having such lists will make your life easier. Doctors appreciate them; and if the EMTs have to come to your house, these documents will make their job easier, too. It's a good idea to put the copies in clear, plastic document protectors. You can buy document protectors at the local office supply store or online. Put one copy of all four lists in your mom's home where they are easily accessible (some people put them on the refrigerator) and make copies for yourself. If you have a computer and a smartphone, put the files on your computer and email them to yourself so that they are accessible on your smartphone. If you don't have a computer, keep a handwritten list somewhere safe and accessible, such as in your handbag or wallet.

5. JOURNAL OF HEALTH CHANGES

This is helpful for doctors, nurses, hospitals, and you. It doesn't have to be elaborate. Just put down the date and a brief description of what happened (e.g., March 18, 2015—Mom fell in the bathroom; taken to hospital, nothing broken, released two days later). Always put down the year. For better or worse, dementia can last for years. And as time goes by, it gets harder to remember what happened when (even if you're young!).

6. HANDICAPPED PARKING PASS

If your mom has trouble getting into or out of the car, or walking long distances across parking lots, you may be able to get a handicapped parking pass for her. Talk to your doctor. If he thinks it's appropriate, he will either give you a letter, or he'll fill out a form to be sent to your state's Department of Motor Vehicles.

7. TRANSPORTATION OPTIONS

Many communities have programs called "mobility buses" or "senior rides" which will transport seniors to and from doctors' appointments and errands, either for free or for a small donation (they will also let caregivers ride with the patient). Check with your local Department of Aging to see what's available.

8. WALKING AIDS

Dozens of different walking aids are available, all the way from canes (at least three kinds to choose from!) to four-wheeled carts with brakes, transportation seats, and baskets. Tesla is probably working on an electric one right now (who knows?). We chose the four-wheeler for Mom, and she loved it. We put a fake tiger tail on the back of it to provide some pizzazz (choosing not to add a bell turned out to be one of our better decisions). The cart allowed her to go all around the house with ease, and safely. The kind you get will be determined by how well your mom is getting around, and how comfortable she is with using a walking aid. You will also have to measure the width of your doorways; you don't want to buy something that won't fit through them. Whatever kind you decide to purchase, you need to get one that your mom likes. Remember: the walking aid, no matter how good or technologically advanced, is no good at all if your mom doesn't like it or doesn't use it. It's also a good idea to get a transport wheelchair in case you need it. Transport wheelchairs are for when you need to get your mom from the house to the car (it's true, you can use a four-wheeled cart since they do fold up; but, in my experience, they are a little heavy and bulky to be carrying around). Medicare or private insurance may cover some of the mobility aids; ask before you buy.

9. GRAB BARS

Grab bars are exactly what they say they are: sturdy bars that are placed on the walls of a house (usually in the bathroom) which can be grabbed onto for balance. They are especially useful in the shower area and around commodes. Most are easy to install, but if you need help, contact your local Department of Aging or community group, since they will sometimes install them for free.

10. HIGH-SEAT TOILETS

Standard toilets, which are low to the ground, can be hard for seniors to sit down on or get up from. High-seat toilets can be purchased and installed, which will make life easier for everyone. If you can't afford a new toilet, you can get an adult potty chair, which has a high seat and which can be fitted over your current toilet. Tip: if you can, buy one potty chair for the toilet, and another one to use elsewhere around the house. Moving a potty chair back and forth between two locations is no fun.

11. ADULT DIAPERS AND "CHUCKS"

Keep some adult diapers around the house in case of emergencies. Some companies will deliver adult diapers to your house on a regular schedule; otherwise, just buy them at a local store. Diapers come "with tabs" and "without tabs"; experiment with both to find out which kind is easiest for you. The same goes for "chucks." These are cotton or polyester pads that you can put on the bed, under the patient, in case of accidents. You can get disposable ones and washable ones; I got some of both.

12. MISCELLANEOUS MEDICAL EQUIPMENT

Thermometers and blood pressure kits are good things to keep on hand. Instructions on how to use them are in the packages, but you can always find instructional videos on the Internet or get advice from your health care provider.

13. SAFE LIFTING AND TRANSFER SKILLS

It is likely that at some point your mom will fall and find herself on the floor. If it is a bad fall—if you suspect that a bone is broken, or if your mom is dazed or confused—call 911. On the other hand, if the fall is not serious, and your mom wants you to help her get up, stop and think before taking any action. You need to know the proper techniques for safe lifting before you act. You can get information on lifting techniques from various places, but the best thing you can do is watch a live demonstration or video of how to get someone back on their feet (or into a chair). Many senior centers and assisted-living centers give one- or two-hour lessons, for free, on how to do this properly. For now, remember this: never lift more than you can comfortably handle, and don't use your back to do heavy lifting. Don't be ashamed to call for help. That is what the EMTs are here for. And there is this: if you hurt yourself lifting your patient, you won't be able to help them—or yourself.

14. SCATTER RUGS

I knew that I would probably lose this battle, but I gave it a try anyway. It is an irrefutably good idea to remove scatter rugs from your house. Those that have adhesive backing on them are still a tripping hazard simply because of their height off the floor; just a quarter of an inch can pose a stumbling block (literally!). But Mom, alas, was ready for me on this one. "I know where every scatter rug is," she pointed out. "I put them there, and they've been there for twenty years. I would trip if they weren't there."

That made sense, even to me.

15. SAFER EATING TECHNIQUES

Many seniors eat too fast or take big bites, all of which can lead to choking. If your mom has started to do this, you can try a couple of things. Give her smaller portions of food, at different intervals, and cut up any big pieces of food, particularly meat. Soft food is easier for seniors to eat and digest, and, depending on what your doctor says, switching to a soft diet might be an option. It's also a good idea to learn the Heimlich maneuver; your local Red Cross can advise you about classes and videos.

16. BALANCING EXERCISES

Many senior centers and exercise centers offer yoga classes that emphasize increasing arm and leg strength and improving balance. These classes are sometimes called "seated" yoga or "restorative" yoga. If your mom is physically able and amenable, she might try one of these classes. They do help. But by the time I learned about them, my mom was past the point where going to an exercise class was an option. Sometimes you see the window of opportunity closing, and you can't stop it.

17. A KING CHARLES CAVALIER SPANIEL

Actually, I'm just kidding on this one. But I can't deny it: having our dog, Clara, around the house helped all of us. She was a true "comfort dog," and she was able to entertain Mom. As to why she always licked Mom's ankle when she (Mom, not Clara) was eating breakfast, we'll never know. But it gave Mom something to laugh about, and that was good enough.

———

I provided you with a lot of information here. But knowing it now may save you time and trouble later. At least I didn't make you read a whole chapter on the anatomy of a whale (for that one, see Mr. Melville).

PART TWO

COPING WITH MIDDLE-STAGE DEMENTIA

"Are these things necessities?
Then let us meet them as necessities."

THE KING TO THE EARL OF WESTMORELAND
Act 3, Scene 1
Henry IV, Part 2
By
William Shakespeare

Chapter Six

Help!

— Finding a Caregiver: The White Whale of Dementia

WE SAW OUR FAMILY DOCTOR, AGAIN, a few weeks later. He looked over the hospital's notes, and he was sympathetic. But without any way to definitely know what Mom had, he couldn't prescribe a cure. He gave us the usual directions: for her to stay hydrated, get rest, and take pain medicine when needed. He was looking at me when he said it. I guess he thought that it was good advice for me, too. And maybe even him.

Our doctor mentioned dementia. Of course, we knew that he was wrong, too.

It was clear, however, that by the time Mom turned eighty-eight, she could no longer live in her home by herself without help. Mom wanted to stay in her own home. She was comfortable and knew where everything was. She'd been living in the farmhouse for more than fifty years (that's half a century!). While David and I spent time at her house, and had her over at our house for what we told Mom were "mini vacations," this was no longer enough. There were times when Mom needed someone to be with her, and David and I couldn't be. And there was this: although Mom wasn't requiring a lot from us now, we were getting tired and needed time off. Caregiver respites are important, and they become more so as time goes by.

We needed to hire someone to come in to help.

In retrospect, we should have gotten help earlier. My conviction that Mom and I could handle everything by ourselves was so wrong. I wasn't trained to help elderly or dementia patients, and I didn't realize that one day Mom would cease to be "Mom" in her mind and in her personality. My lifelong companion would be gone. I'd be caring for a stranger. The moral of this is simple: get help early. And after you get help, get more help.

My first thought was that I would find someone to come in part-time, maybe a few hours a week. That would have been ideal for Mom, and for us, for several reasons. First, Mom didn't need a lot done for her, and a couple of hours a day would be more than enough to ensure that she was okay. Second, Mom wasn't used to having strangers in the house, and David and I figured that a few hours a day would be all that she would tolerate without a struggle. Third, the hourly price almost knocked me to the floor. More on that later.

It was not hard finding an agency that specialized in sending caregivers to provide in-home help. In fact, once I started looking, I must have gotten on a mailing list, because soon caregiver agencies were calling and emailing *me*. So, things were looking up. I had a lot of agencies to choose from, and all their caregivers had been vetted, trained, insured, and came with a list of references. The agencies had done all the work that I would have had to do if I were hiring someone on my own. What could go wrong?

Well . . . from the start, I found out that the schedule we were asking for (a few hours a week) would be difficult to accommodate. Most caregivers want full-time employment. Another sizable number of caregivers want to work only in the mornings, or in the afternoons. Almost none of them work on weekends.

I learned that, amazingly, caregivers are people

just like me. Who knew? They want steady employment. They often hold more than one job, and some of them are going to school at night, training for a better job. Why would they want a better job? Because caregiving is a tough, unpredictable, and sometimes frightening job. The caregiver never knows what they will face with their patient on any given day. Dementia poses extra challenges.

I don't know what kind of health insurance the caregivers we met had. I was afraid to ask.

And as far as a salary goes … many of them are paid minimum wage, if that. The high prices we were being charged reflected the money that the agencies needed for overhead—all the time-consuming things (vetting, training, and insuring) that I was happy to let them do. Neither Medicare, nor Mom's private health insurance, helped pay for this care, which is defined as "activities of daily living," or ADLs. (Important note: please check with Medicare and/or your private health insurance agencies, because regulations and policies are changing, especially since COVID-19.) At the prices we were paying, I began to wonder how long our money would hold out.

At this point, I was still concerned about how much money we were spending. It was an attitude that was about to change.

Nevertheless, we did find some caregivers who were willing to try out the several-hours-a-week routine. I use the word "some" because I soon found out that hiring "one" caregiver actually meant hiring "many" caregivers. This is because . . .wait for it . . . I learned, once again, that caregivers are like us. They have doctors' appointments to go to; they get sick, themselves; their cars break down; they have family emergencies.

The good thing about hiring from an agency is that if your regular caregiver can't come, the agency can usually find another caregiver to fill in for them temporarily. The bad thing about hiring from an agency is that . . . please see the sentence above. It's a double-edged sword.

It seemed that as soon as Mom got used to one caregiver, she had to get used to another, and another, and another. This was hard on Mom. She was a kind and generous person, but having a slew of different caregivers coming in and out was confusing, especially to someone with the onset of dementia. And, try as she might, she couldn't keep their names or personalities straight. Neither, it turned out, could I. I had to keep a log of all the different caregivers who showed up. I must have given my "Introduction to Mom 101" speech so often, to so many different caregivers, that I probably said it in my sleep.

After a month or two of trying out our part-time routine, we graduated to the every-afternoon-a-week schedule, in the hope that we could achieve more stability in the number of caregivers who came. We couldn't. So, we expanded to several days a week, and finally, to a full-time, almost round-the-clock schedule. Although the prices went up (way up!), the results were the same. We couldn't seem to keep one caregiver continuously. And with round-the-clock care, every shift would, of necessity, have a new caregiver on duty. Mom would go to bed with one caregiver and get up with another. This was anxiety that Mom didn't need.

I talked to other people using caregiver agencies, and I even switched to a different caregiver agency. The results were the same.

It was no one's fault. The agencies did their best with the employees that they had. The caregivers did their best, but . . . many of them were young, and unfamiliar with the problems of the elderly. They didn't have much in common with Mom, and had trouble coping with her symptoms (not that anyone blamed them; even some nurses and doctors have difficulty dealing with dementia patients). The caregivers also had their own problems, which they sometimes brought with them (yes, just like us).

So we looked at different approaches. One agency specialized in live-in caregivers. That sounded good, but the farmhouse wasn't a modern house and I doubted that it was suitable for a boarder. Also, the price tag was astronomical (I'm still worried about money, right?). Our second approach involved the county Department of Aging. They kept a list of vetted, but not insured, home health care workers who had received training, and who had references. They were often older women, and that, from Mom's perspective, was a plus. We interviewed a number of women and hired one of them, part-time. If you go this route, you need to do thorough interviews. The Department of Aging will often provide you with a checklist of things you need to ask prospective caregivers. Don't be shy. You may not be comfortable talking about personal matters, but asking things such as "What is your favorite color?" won't cut it. Get their references. And call their references. You may find out important information. All of this takes time.

If your mom is fearful of strangers, as my mom soon became, it might be difficult to get her to accept a caregiver. We solved this problem by introducing her new caregiver as a neighbor. You can also say that the caregiver is a family friend, if that works for you. Yes, sometimes the truth is overrated (but don't quote me on that).

Encourage your caregiver to start a journal, or at least write down how your mom is during the day when you are not around. It's helpful to see the progression of your mom's condition from an unbiased point of view.

There is another piece of advice regarding caregivers that might be helpful to you. If you hire a caregiver, and you plan to go away for several days, do a trial run first. Just spend a day and night someplace near your house. You'll be able to see what kinds of problems or questions come up, and how your mom reacts when you're absent. If you do go on vacation, give a temporary power of attorney for medical decisions to either the caregiver, a neighbor, a family member, or someone else you trust.

To recap: hiring a health care worker for a patient with dementia can be a hit-or-miss proposition. It can consume a lot of time before you find the right caregiver or agency. Some astounding caregiver successes do exist, such as the older woman who cared for one of my uncles during the latter part of his life, and who was dependable, honest, and helpful. And there are disasters, like the time David and I were halfway to Pennsylvania when we got a call saying that the caregiver for Mom couldn't come that day. Finding a good caregiver is akin to searching for the Holy Grail. Check all the resources you can: agencies, senior centers, churches, friends, the Department of Aging. Always keep looking.

Things went well with our new caregiver for a while. We were able to relax. David and I went on a few daytrips. But she had to quit after a month because of a family emergency, and we had to start all over again—a situation we were now familiar with.

We tried, but, after a year of working with many different caregivers, we were tired. Mom was confused and unhappy.

It was time for Plan B.

CHAPTER SEVEN

MOVING OUT, AND MOVING IN

Resistance Is Futile

A MOMENT COMES, I suppose, in everyone's life when you get an idea so brilliant, so timely, and so revolutionary that you wonder why the Nobel Prize committee isn't waiting at your front door with a check and a gold medal.

Hopefully, that moment will pass.

In my case, it did not.

I had such an idea, and it went like this: if finding a reliable, in-home caregiver was so hard, why not move Mom into our house so that we could be her caregivers? We could eliminate the middleman, care for Mom as only her children could, and save money to boot. Go ahead and book that flight to Sweden!

Those of you who have been reading this handbook from the beginning (congratulations, by the way!) are probably saying to yourselves, *She's still trying to save money, isn't she?* And to you I say, "Hang in there. That moment of reckoning is coming."

Some of you may also have picked up on the phrase, "care for Mom as only her children could." It's worth thinking about this for a moment. I had no medical training or experience. After retiring from my day job, I had taken up writing and had achieved some success, but this vocation required hours of quiet time for me, on my computer, in the spare bedroom upstairs. I was not a particularly good cook or housekeeper. Nor was I known for my exceptional patience. But I had seen how the other caregivers did it, right? How hard could it be?

I guess you can see where I am going with this. Loving your mom is one thing. Caring for her emotional and physical needs, on a full-time basis, is something else. I was about to get a lesson in the difference.

—

We interrupt this program for a special announcement:

Before we go any further, I want to explain why we didn't consider moving Mom into an assisted-living community. Many such facilities exist in our area, some of which have memory care units with excellent reputations. But long ago, after Dad had died and when Mom was still in good health, I had made a promise to her. "You'll never have to leave your home, Mom. I'll never put you away." That was my sacred promise to Mom, in blunt words that we both understood.

That promise was now untenable. I would have to break it. And a lot of agonizing and remorse, on my part, followed. Doubt about what I did continues to this day.

The moral of the story is this: try not to make promises that you may have to break later on. You don't know what's going to happen in the future. Be open to new possibilities. There might be a Plan C that is better than your Plan A or your Plan B.

—

We now continue with our regularly scheduled programming:

On the brighter side, while Mom would be leaving her home, she would be going to a comfortable home that she knew well; her family would be with her; and her own home, relatives, friends,

44

and local interests would not be far away. Anyone would be happy with that, right?

Anyone might. But not Mom.

I had mentioned to her the possibility of moving in with us a number of times and had been met with opposition. Now, however, I realized that I had to convince her that this was the right thing to do. I couldn't make her come if she didn't want to, and she had enough presence of mind to resist me. I had visions of Mom calling the police and having me arrested for elder abuse. So, like any daughter would do, I began devising a number of lies that I could use to trick her into coming to our house. (Remember, I was going to "care for Mom as only her own children could.")

These lies varied in complexity and plausibility, from "your house has to be fumigated for termites" to "the Government has determined that you live in a Terrorist Class 1 Area and everyone has to be evacuated." As it turned out, I had to use only a "modified" lie. Mom began to have real difficulty getting out of bed because of dizziness, and one or two times she fell back on the bed while trying to get up. I suggested that she come to my house for a month to rest and recuperate, in hopes that the dizzy spells would pass. To my surprise, she agreed.

I should have thought more about the significance of Mom's answer, but I didn't. In hindsight, I can see that Mom now knew that something serious was wrong with her, and that she was frightened.

And so it was that, two days later, we packed enough clothes for Mom for a month, got her medicines rounded up, and drove her to our house, twenty minutes away.

We were entering uncharted territory, and a guiding star was hard to find.

Chapter Eight

Home Is Where You Are

"I'm on strike" (Mom)

OUR HOUSE WAS READY. We gave Mom our first-floor bedroom with a big bathroom, and David and I moved into an upstairs bedroom. We put a baby monitor in Mom's room so she could easily talk to us if we were upstairs. This turned out to be more important than we would have guessed. Mom would often wake up frightened, in the middle of the night, but with the baby monitor on she could call out to us, and either David or I could go downstairs and reassure her that everything was okay. In addition, she had a personal alarm system that she wore around her neck; she had had this system in her house, and she brought it with her. I had already done most of the things suggested in Chapter Three.

Mom loved dogs, and she and our spaniel, Clara, got along fine. I think that Clara provided a much-needed distraction for her, as well as an escape from the troubles of the present.

Mom enjoyed listening to church services on Sunday via the radio. We made sure that she could continue to do that. If your mom is religious, accommodate her wishes and needs in this regard as best you can. You won't regret it. One of my memories of Mom at this time is hearing her sing the hymns along with the choir on the radio. These are the kinds of memories you need.

After a few weeks at our house, the dizzy spells lessened, and Mom felt better. Her daily schedule was simple. She got up in the morning around 9 a.m. and came out to the kitchen to get her cereal and a small glass of orange juice. I got her coffee. Our coffee maker was different from hers, and I could see that, at this point, it was hard for Mom to learn new things. Following breakfast, I would clean up the dishes and get her pills for her. Lunch was easy: I would make her a chicken or ham salad sandwich and get her a Diet Coke. In the afternoon we might go outside for a walk, using her four-wheeled cart, and be back in time for her soap opera, *General Hospital*. Dinner consisted of either something that I had made, or one of a variety of small TV dinners, and another Diet Coke. After more medicines, she would get cleaned up; usually, this meant a sponge bath using the sink. Afterwards I would bring her a small bowl of sugar-free cookies and ice cream. She would take it to her room, and bring her bowl out to me when she was done. Then she would watch a little TV in her room (usually the news, *Wheel of Fortune*, and *Jeopardy!*), and go to bed around 7 p.m. I should also mention that Mom had cookie snacks throughout the day. We made sure that cookies were always on the counter for her.

No, this was not a medically-sanctioned, nutritious diet. But it was what Mom would eat, and she enjoyed it. In the beginning of her illness, I talked about her diet with a number of doctors. One of them told me: "Don't fight it. This is one battle you don't need and can't win. Let her eat what she wants. And be glad that she is still eating." This was some of the best advice that I got on the subject.

Mom was able to do a lot for herself, and what she asked of me was not difficult or time consuming. And yet . . . it is different when you bring another person into your home. A new dynamic is created, and you have to adapt. Some of the small, crazy things that bothered me I could fix: for example, giving Mom a paper cereal bowl instead of a china one to prevent her from banging the sides of the dish. Or, since Mom didn't always like what we had on TV, I would watch what I wanted on my computer, or just do something else. These were small things. But if you can fix the little things, do it. Because you won't have much control over the big ones.

As our routine became established, and Mom improved, David and I began to think that things were progressing well. That is until one morning, when Mom came out of her bedroom, sat on the living room sofa, and did not ask for breakfast. When I asked why she was sitting there, she replied, "I'm on strike."

It took some back-and-forth negotiation before I got the full story. Mom looked me in the eye and said in a strong voice, "I'm not eating until you take me back to my farmhouse."

Well. It turns out that what one person thinks of as an amicable arrangement may be intolerable to someone else. All this time Mom had been seething inside, wanting to be at her own house and not wanting to live at ours.

This was a revelation, and it taught me something. Your mom may be ill. She may not be reasonable or coherent at times. But she still has ideas and feelings, and she still wants to do what she wants to do. She's been around longer than you have, and she probably knows more than you do, even if she can't remember it all. She's an adult with needs, although her mind and her communication skills may be declining. She's still a person with dignity, and needs to be treated like one.

I knew that Mom couldn't go home, and I suspect that, somewhere inside herself, she knew it, too. We reached a compromise: I would drive her to the farmhouse once a week, at least, and we would spend the morning or the afternoon there. She would be reassured that everything was just as she had left it, and she could still enjoy her home.

Respect and compromise. Sometimes they're the best words in the English language.

Chapter Nine

Call Me Ishmael

What Did You Say Your Name Was?

The first year at our house passed without much angst, mainly because Mom was still "Mom" and could do many things for herself. But the "I'm on strike" episode was an eye-opener: I wondered if Mom was keeping other things from me. Did she have other feelings and thoughts that she wasn't sharing?

Now that I saw her 24/7, I began to notice changes in her behavior. They confirmed what the experts said: that while dementia patients could have brief periods of good mental and physical health, the downhill slide couldn't be reversed.

Mom had always had a reputation for cleanliness. The "cleanest person in Severn," we called her. Throughout her whole life Mom was immaculate, both personally and in her household. If something in the kitchen was dirty, she washed it right away. In the hot, humid summers, with no indoor air conditioning and dust blowing in from the fields, she had been known to take two baths a day. My sister and I used to laugh.

At our house, Mom had assumed responsibility for cleaning herself, either using the shower with help from me, or taking sponge baths using the sink. Getting into and out of the tub was not an option anymore. She seemed to be doing a good job getting herself cleaned up every night, but the thing was, *she never asked for help*. I began to wonder. Towels in the bathroom were never very wet. The shower stall was so clean it didn't seem as if anyone was using it. When I would ask her about it (always in the form of an innocent question, such as, "Can I help you wash your hair today?") she always insisted that everything was fine and that she didn't need me. But although Mom appeared clean, I was worried. It was apparent that she had curtailed her personal cleaning regimen and would not tell me.

I learned later that an aversion to bathing and washing is common for dementia patients. I managed to persuade Mom to let me use a warm hand cloth to wash her. This felt good to her, and so she allowed me to do it. Washing her hair was a different matter. I finally bought one of the "dry shampoos" and used it. I wasn't keen on the idea of putting dry chemicals on Mom's head, but it was better than nothing. And it did help.

The other thing that was concerning was that Mom resisted leaving the house, particularly for doctor appointments. Part of her reluctance was understandable. It was often hard to get her ready on time—something always seemed to come up—and she could never decide on what to wear. But the biggest problem was Mom's attitude. The bottom line was that she didn't want to go to the doctor's anymore. She said that she had had enough of doctors, and it was time for her to quit. I have to say, I admired her grit.

I decided that if I couldn't make her go to the doctor, I would have the doctor come to us. I can almost hear you saying: "What? Are you out of your mind?" But here's a piece of information that may surprise you: you can find doctors who make house calls. Such a service is a lifesaver, one you won't regret using.

My search for a house-call practice was initially frustrating. Mom's own primary care doctor did not make house calls. He couldn't give me the names of any doctors that did. I looked on the web but found nothing. So, I started calling around to people I knew, asking if they had heard of anyone. And one of them had. I called the number that they gave me, explained our situation, and in two days Mom had a house call from her new doctor. Voilà!

Here's the thing: medical practices that do house calls are in high demand. You don't often find them listed on the web because they don't need to advertise. They have all the business they want, and more. They know what we all know: patients would much rather see the doctor in the comfort of their own home. That's actually how it used to be in the olden days, isn't it? So, while you may have to do a little digging for information, don't give up. Use every resource you have. You will find one. (P.S.— When you find your house-call practice, they may have information on other house-call doctors, such as podiatrists. Once that magic door is opened, you're likely to find all kinds of resources.)

Our house-call doctor could do everything Mom's previous doctor could do, including writing and calling in prescriptions, taking blood, and filling out insurance papers. The practice had a contract with an X-ray company to take X-rays in our own home. They accepted both Medicare and private insurance. In my experience, the house-call doctor was no more expensive than her regular doctor: we paid little or nothing at all.

The benefits of having a house-call doctor take care of an elderly person, or an ill person of any age, are hard to overestimate. For starters, the doctor sees her patient in her own environment, obtaining a unique perspective on how the patient lives. You don't have to go out in bad weather and sit in a doctor's waiting room listening to other people cough. The doctor isn't rushed and can spend more than 15 minutes with the patient. That private, one-on-one relationship is priceless.

For the sake of confidentiality, I will call Mom's new house-call doctor Dr. Jan, but she knows who she is. The day she rang our doorbell, I celebrated. Thank you, wherever you are, Dr. Jan!

The doctor got a thorough picture of Mom's condition, her health history, and her current lifestyle, and she left me with a ton of suggestions and pamphlets about aging and dementia. One of them was about the prevention of urinary tract infections, or UTIs, in the elderly. It was something that I had never thought about, but it turns out that UTIs can cause symptoms which either mimic dementia or complicate its symptoms. Dr. Jan was a tremendous help to me and to Mom.

Nevertheless ... in the second year I witnessed more changes in Mom. She began taking more naps, fewer walks, and preferred to stay in her room most of the time. I believe that she felt safe in her own room, and that was good enough for me. I brought her meals in to her, and in the evening, I put her cookies, and Coke and water, near the bed in case she got hungry or thirsty during the night. The most startling development was that she stopped asking to go to the farm for her weekly visit. I'd ask her if she wanted to go, and she would say, "Not now." I didn't realize it at the time, but what Mom actually meant was, "Not ever again." This was sadder than I could have ever imagined. Even though the weekly visits had been time-consuming, I grieved when they came to an end.

Mom also stopped watching TV. First, she stopped watching the news, and later, her soap opera. In hindsight, I think I can understand what was happening: she could no longer make sense of all the people and the events on the television screen.

Her diet became stranger. Breakfast and lunch stayed pretty much the same, but she stopped drinking coffee. She wanted only one thing for dinner: pancakes. I stuck with the advice an earlier doctor had given us: don't fight it. Pancakes it was.

With all the obvious things that I was noticing, I wondered how much else was going on that I was missing. I found out one evening, after I had persuaded Mom to come out to the kitchen and eat her pancakes with David and me. During the middle of the meal, Mom looked up and asked David, "Who are you?"

It's hard to describe our stunned silence. Mom was completely serious. David tried to make a joke and said something like, "Well, I live here," to which Mom responded, "Are you married?"

Mom had completely lost her memory. An hour later, however, it came back and she knew who we were again. More of these episodes started happening. One time, she couldn't remember what a pancake was called; on another, she called me "Lisa." On still another occasion, talking to her, I sensed that she was drifting away, and I asked her, "Mom, do you know what my name is?" She studied my face for a few minutes and said, "You know, it's on the tip of my tongue." I laughed. So did she.

I began going through photograph albums with her, pointing out people she knew and naming them for her in case she couldn't. We turned to a picture of Dad and one of his beagles (we called him "Hodges Mobutu, Dog of the Nile" for reasons too complicated—and nutty—to repeat here). Dad and

Hodges had had many adventures together, and I began telling her one of our old, family stories about them. Mom listened carefully and then advised me, "Oh, that wasn't him. That was my other husband."

Important announcement: if Mom's "other husband" is out there somewhere reading this, please do not contact me.

The behavioral changes didn't stop. Her sense of humor was fading. Her memory came and went. Some nights she would wake up, get out of bed, and walk into the living room and stand there. We began leaving a light on in the living room at night, and we also posted a big piece of paper on the inside of her bedroom door which said, "It's Night-Time—Go Back to Bed." That actually worked for quite a while.

A friend of ours, Erma, had just had a serious stroke, and she described the resulting hard times that had followed her illness by saying, "My life came apart." That's a pretty good description of what dementia was doing to Mom. One of our last real conversations as mother and daughter came one afternoon, when we were sitting in the living room. She turned to me and said, "Leona, I don't know what's happening to me. Something's wrong with my brain."

She knew.

PART THREE

FACING SEVERE DEMENTIA, AND THE END

"We see which way the stream of time doth run"

ARCHBISHOP SCROOP TO WESTMORELAND
Act 4, Scene 1

"He's walked the way of nature"

EARL OF WARWICK TO THE CHIEF JUSTICE
Act 5, Scene 2

"His cares are now all ended"

EARL OF WARWICK TO THE CHIEF JUSTICE
Act 5, Scene 2
Henry IV, Part 2
By
William Shakespeare

CHAPTER TEN

THE BREAK

THERE HAVE ONLY BEEN A FEW TIMES IN MY LIFE when I have been well and truly frightened. The episode below is one of those times.

It was a summer's afternoon in June. The weather was cool enough that I had some of the windows open. I was in the living room reading. David was at the kitchen table doing some research on his computer. Clara was dozing in her dog basket by his side.

I heard Mom come out of her bedroom. I knew right away that something was odd, because Mom was usually napping at this time of day. I watched as she wheeled her cart into the kitchen and opened the refrigerator door. She stood motionless for a moment, looking inside the refrigerator, then shut the door and walked toward David and me. (Years later I wondered if she got mad because there were no crab cakes in the fridge; but, maybe not.)

"I'm calling the police," she said. She was almost shouting. "You've kidnapped me, and you're keeping me here against my will. I'm getting out now, and you can't stop me." The anger—and hatred—in her voice were horrific. She pressed the life-alert-system button hanging around her neck and told the operator that we were trying to kill her.

It's hard to describe what happened next. I ran over to her and tried to reassure her, saying, "You're okay, Mom, you're in our house and you're safe here with David and me." Mom said something vile, I don't remember what, and pushed me backward, hard, so that she could get around me and reach the front door.

I didn't fall down. Mom weighed less than 100 pounds. But those 100 pounds packed more strength than I could ever have imagined.

David jumped up to get between Mom and the front door. He had only said a few words to her when Mom grabbed the hair on his head and yanked it, knocking off his glasses. He yelped and she let go, still heading straight for the door.

By this time my mind had started to function. I knew Mom couldn't get to the phone, and that once outside she wouldn't be able to go far. I also knew that we needed help, desperately, because we couldn't control her, and because she might hurt herself or us. I told David, "Call 911 and ask for help so that we can get her to the hospital." But the phone had already started ringing.

David rushed to answer it. It was the life-alert-system people. David took care of them while I overtook Mom, opened the front door, and told her that she could go out. Once outside, she continued to accuse me of kidnapping her and screamed, in the direction of the neighbors, that she needed the police. Being outside, however, slowed her down a little, and she began to look around her, as if she had never seen our front yard before. She never stopped shouting for the police.

David had managed to call 911 for an ambulance. The dispatcher asked David to describe what was going on, and he did. The dispatcher said that he would take care of it. A few minutes later two police cars rolled into our driveway, sirens on. The dispatcher—bless his heart—had logged the call as a domestic dispute and acted accordingly.

You can imagine how I felt when I saw the police cars show up. My first reaction was, believe it or not: *What are the neighbors going to think?* My second reaction was, Mom had gotten her wish—the police had arrived.

Lord only knows what Mom thought.

In any case, as the two police officers came walking down the sidewalk, Mom quieted down. David, by now, was on the front porch with us, and he stood near Mom to make sure that she didn't fall.

I told the police officers about Mom's violent behavior and her illness, and that I wanted to get her to the hospital to be evaluated. They were sympathetic. But they informed me that regulations prohibited them from taking Mom to the ER against her will. The only way they could do what I was asking would be if I went with them to the county courthouse and got a court order declaring Mom to be mentally incompetent.

Well. It is strange how the mind works. A few minutes ago, I had been visualizing the possible injuries and deaths of Mom, David, and/or me. Now I was discussing the mission of the county police, to include legal considerations and protections for the elderly, with two nice, young policemen I'd never seen before. The three of us could have been filming a panel discussion for a TV show. It was that surreal.

The situation with Mom continued to evolve. One of the policemen asked Mom if she wanted to sit in the car with him for a while, and she said no. She said she wanted to sit down on the front porch, and David helped her sit on the steps. The sun was out, and the steps were warm. She grew quiet, and the anger seemed to drain out of her.

The policemen stayed for a while and I know that we talked, although I have no memory of what we said. David and I led Mom back into the house, and they left. Mom lay down on the bed and promptly took a nap.

I called Dr. Jan and told her what had happened. She wrote a prescription for a mild anti-psychotic medicine, gave me directions on how and when to use it, and called it in to the pharmacy for us to pick up. Dr. Jan said that if anything else happened to call her immediately and she would come over; otherwise, she would see us tomorrow morning. Dr. Jan had seen this kind of thing before, and thought that Mom, with the aid of the new medicine, would probably be calm for the rest of the day and night.

She was right. Mom slept most of the rest of the afternoon. She woke up around dinner time, and I brought pancakes to her. When I asked her how she was feeling, she said that she was fine. She ate her ice cream and cookies, and she went to bed. She slept through the night until morning.

She had no recollection of what had happened.

I realized that Mom wasn't "Mom" anymore. Mom was gone. Someone else had taken her place.

CHAPTER ELEVEN

LEWY WHO?

". . . and flights of angels sing thee to thy rest"
— William Shakespeare

THE NEXT MORNING DR. JAN CAME. Mom had woken up and had eaten breakfast. When she learned that Dr. Jan had arrived to check on her, she was initially resistant, and in the "I'm done with doctors" mode. But when Dr. Jan walked into her bedroom, she relented. About the only thing that she had to say to either of us was, "I'm fine." All of Mom's vital signals were good. She was weaker, though, and quieter than usual.

After Dr. Jan finished examining Mom, she and I sat down in the kitchen. We talked about yesterday's psychotic episode, and how Mom did not remember any of it—or so she said. Dr. Jan explained that in some types of dementia, such as Lewy body dementia, or LBD, short, psychotic episodes were one of the symptoms. She suspected that Mom had LBD.

According to some sources, LBD is one of the leading forms of dementia, with Alzheimer's being the most common. It is normally characterized by physical weakness, gait imbalance, memory loss that comes and goes, hallucinations, delusions, and psychotic breaks. It can only be definitely diagnosed by an autopsy and examination of the brain. To be blunt: you have to be dead before you can find out what's wrong with you.

Doctor Jan, after discussing how Mom's symptoms aligned with those of LBD, provided us with advice, reading material, and links to relevant websites. I did my homework and was disheartened to learn that, like other types of dementia, there was no cure for LBD. But I also felt confident that Doctor Jan and her team were giving Mom her best chance to live as long and as comfortably as possible. That was one reason why I didn't consider taking Mom to a specialist. Mom's age, her frailty, and the fact that she became upset and confused when faced with new situations were other reasons. But not every case is the same, and there's not one right answer for everyone. In many cases, taking a dementia patient to a specialist is a wise thing to do. There are many dementia specialists out there and new information is being discovered all the time. Talk to your primary care physician; they will guide you and provide you with references.

Dr. Jan confirmed that episodes such as the one Mom had experienced were dangerous, and for that reason anti-psychotic medicines were needed. Many such drugs were on the market, and the trick was to find the one which worked best (because some of the drugs, in some of the patients, made things worse—a whole lot worse). Dr. Jan pointed out that, although it was early yet, Mom seemed to be tolerating well the particular drug and dosage that she had prescribed. But we would have to keep a close eye on Mom and be ready to adjust her medicine if any sudden changes in her behavior occurred. The side effect of the current drug, so far, seemed to be that Mom was more tired than usual.

It was then that Dr. Jan and I had "the talk." It was about hospice care. Dr. Jan explained how it worked, and how it could help all of us. Below are the things that I learned. Note: I believe that this information is still correct as of June 2020. But things change, so, if you are considering hospice care, ask about the rules and regulations in your state to make sure that you have the most accurate information.

I had heard a lot about hospice care over the years, and most of what I thought I knew about it was wrong. Here are some of the important points:

1. Though you must have a prognosis of six months or less to live to be admitted into hospice care, it doesn't mean that a patient can't live beyond six months to remain under hospice care. Some people have been under their care for years.

2. While it is good to have a doctor's referral, you don't need one. You can call them on the phone yourself.

3. You can be treated in a hospital while under hospice care. But, before you take your patient to the hospital, you need to have the approval of your hospice if you want to stay in that hospice.

4. You can leave Hospice at any time. You can also come back at any time, as long as your prognosis is six months or less.

5. Hospices often have a separate facility

dedicated to hospice care. They also provide in-home services.

6. Hospice doctors and nurses do many of the same things that your own non-hospice practitioner does; it's just their focuses and purposes are different. You can still keep your own non-hospice practitioner when you are in hospice care. They will coordinate with the hospice nurses. In my experience, Medicare and Mom's private insurance covered both.

7. Hospice care is for people who have a terminal disease and who are not seeking a cure.

8. Hospice care is for people who want to remain as comfortable as possible as their disease progresses. The idea is to prolong the best quality of life possible and maintain it until the end.

9. Medicare and most insurances pay for hospice care.

When Dr. Jan left, she said that she would start the paperwork for hospice care. The next day a hospice nurse came, her arms filled with notebooks and medical bags. It was that fast.

I can't stress enough the benefits, expert help, and sheer peace of mind that hospice care provides. It took only an hour or so for us to sign the forms and go over the regulations. One of the first things that we did was put up a "Do Not Resuscitate" sign on the refrigerator and on the door to Mom's room. It's a sad sign. Try not to let it get you down. It's necessary, because if EMTs come into your house, they will do everything possible to keep your patient alive. That's what they are trained to do, and we are all glad for this. But those life-saving measures may make the quality of your patient's life truly miserable, and much worse than it was before. The "Do Not Resuscitate" sign is not a sign of failure, or defeat, or abandonment. It is a sign which says, "We accept the inevitable, and we don't want any more suffering."

Our hospice nurse (let's call her Dr. Meg, because that's how we explained her to Mom) gave Mom a thorough examination, which Mom did not enjoy but which she allowed. Dr. Meg surveyed Mom's room and gave me some suggestions. Mom had always slept on the edge of her bed, not a particularly good idea. But, no matter how many times I pulled her into the middle of the bed, she would be on the edge again by morning. Dr. Meg advised that we should get some bed rails. We did, and they helped. Dr. Meg noted that soon Mom would not be able to get in and out of her favorite chair because it was too soft, so we got some stiff cushions and special rails for that chair, too. The latter came from the local medical supplies store. We put our potty chair next to the bed, in case Mom couldn't make it to the bathroom. Dr. Meg also noted that, at some point, Mom might need a hospital bed, so we got one. We rented it by the month. The bed was not comfortable, and Mom didn't like it and, mostly, never used it. It became indispensable later on, though.

Dr. Meg promised that, for now, either she or another nurse would come twice a week. As the situation progressed, nurses might come more frequently. Mom was to stay on the medical regimen that Dr. Jan had prescribed until further notice. Dr. Jan and Dr. Meg would both be on the case and share notes. Dr. Meg emphasized that, although Mom seemed calm now, no one knew what tomorrow would bring. In fact, from that day on, no one really knew what Mom was thinking. She was a polite, quiet stranger who happened to be living in our home. Dr. Meg told us that we could call the hospice number at any time, day or night, for help. They would walk us through what was happening or send someone to the house if need be.

And there was this: Mom could not be left alone, day or night.

I had begun thinking about our new schedule when the phone rang. It was a neighbor who knew a nurse (let's call her Kim) who had just retired and who might want some part-time employment. Would I be interested in talking to her? And so it was that, the following week, we hired Kim to come in and stay with Mom two afternoons a week (this was expanded to three, and later, four). So, in the space of one week, I had not only Dr. Jan, but also Dr. Meg and Nurse Kim coming in, giving help, advice, and encouragement.

Sometimes the cavalry, and their guiding angels, really do arrive. When they do, it's a blessing.

Chapter Twelve

When the Curtain Goes Down

. . . But The Actor Is Still on Stage

A NEW NORMAL WAS ESTABLISHED IN OUR HOUSE. Dr. Jan came every three weeks, Dr. Meg twice a week, and Nurse Kim two or three times a week. We tried to stagger their visits so that they didn't overlap. At times it seemed as if our house was a train station, with all the people coming and going. After a week or so we just left the front door unlocked during the day. After all, what could happen, aside from criminals coming in to steal the silverware? *Just let them try*, I thought. They'd take one look at what was going on and head for the hills. Clara, who loved all people, was, of course, delighted with all of her visitors. Each one who arrived meant more attention for her.

It was odd, but despite all the activity, and the knowledge that Mom's dementia was worsening, our house grew calmer. Mom was withdrawn more than usual, probably because of the anti-psychotic medicine. She was glad to take her morning and afternoon naps, and she enjoyed it when I covered her up with her favorite blanket. She still liked her meals, despite the fact that they consisted of mostly cereal or pancakes. After each meal she would say, "That was good."

One time, apropos of nothing, Mom looked up from her dinner and told me, "Everything counts." I mentioned this episode earlier in the book, but I'd like to repeat it here. I don't know what Mom had in mind, but it's a good philosophy to remember, especially as it applies to dementia (no humor intended). Any action, no matter how small, that you can take to improve your mom's life will be appreciated. Everything counts.

Something else was peculiar. Mom never complained about pain. When I think back on it, this was astounding. Every human being on earth has aches and pains, right? Mom, who was frail and could only get around with her walker, must have had her share. The only three possibilities that I could come up with were: she had no pain; she had pain but wouldn't tell me; or she had pain and couldn't tell me. I'll never know which it was.

For eight months or so our little group (Dr. Jan, Dr. Meg, Nurse Kim, David, Clara, and I) had a surprisingly peaceful existence. Mom did not seem to know who any of us were, or what was happening, but it didn't seem to bother her. Maybe ignorance is bliss. And if this was her new reality, well, it didn't seem to be that bad. I had successfully deluded myself that this period of tranquility could go on indefinitely.

One day I got a glimpse of my real mom— the mom that I knew before dementia. I had been washing her legs with a soft, warm rag, and I made a joke about how skinny her legs were. I think I called her a "skinny minnie." When I looked up, she was smiling, and she had a genuine look of recognition in her eyes—for a brief moment she was Mom again. I am glad that I had that last look from her.

That evening, around 7:30 p.m. or so, after Mom had gone to bed, David and I were in the living room watching TV. I heard Mom get up. This wasn't unusual, since Mom got up to go to the bathroom several times a night. I could always hear her because her four-wheeled walker thumped and clicked as the wheels turned. But instead of heading for the bathroom, I could hear the walker moving toward the windows at the other side of her bedroom. *That's odd*, I thought.

Then I heard it. It wasn't Mom's usual "slide to the floor and everything is okay" fall. This was a loud, hard thud.

When David and I opened the bedroom door, Mom was on the floor, flat on her back, the walker nearby. Mom was trying to get up by herself, but she couldn't. Her left leg wouldn't move. David rolled over the wheelchair and, as carefully as he could, he lifted Mom into it.

We rolled her into the living room, and I gave her some Tylenol. Mom was agitated and wanted us to put her on the sofa. We didn't do that for fear of making her injury worse. I had already called the hospice, and a duty nurse was on her way. But a bad storm was sweeping through the area. All the duty nurses were out on other calls. One would be at our house as soon as she could.

It's an undeniable fact: there's always a bad storm outside when something like this happens. And it always happens in the dead of night. If any of you have ever had a major crisis on a warm, sunny day at 10 a.m., I'd like to hear about it.

Meanwhile, Mom continued to plead to be put on the couch. It was awful.

A little before midnight the nurse arrived. She helped us get Mom into the hospital bed, safely, and examined her. She told us that the injury to Mom's leg needed to be X-rayed. She would make arrangements for an X-ray team, and equipment, to come to our house tomorrow. In the meantime, the nurse prepared some morphine and gave it to Mom, who went right to sleep. The nurse also prepared extra morphine doses for me to give Mom every four hours, if needed. Then the nurse left us, facing into the driving wind and rain, to minister to another household in trouble. I never found out her name. But I will be ever grateful that she came.

The next morning I gave Mom something to drink and a dose of the morphine. She was alert, and talking, and wanted to know why she couldn't move her leg. The X-ray team arrived. After they had finished, the technician called me over. You know how, when you have X-rays at a clinic or hospital, they won't tell you anything and always say, "These X-rays must be sent away to be examined"? Not this time. The technician showed me the X-rays of Mom's leg. When I saw them I nearly fainted. Even I, who knew nothing of what an X-ray of the leg should look like, could see a large space where two bones should have met, but didn't. "It's a fractured head of the femur," he said. "I'll contact the hospice, and someone will be over right away."

When they left, Mom was still alert and, unaccountably, cheerful. She looked at me and said, "I asked the man how my X-ray was, and he said that it was a good X-ray. My leg is going to be just fine." I nodded, in awe of Mom's optimism. It was more than she had said in a week. Of course, the X-ray technician had meant only that his X-rays had come out fine, but I wasn't about to tell Mom that.

I continued to give Mom the morphine that the duty nurse had prescribed, but I could see that Mom was growing more uncomfortable. She kept trying to move her bad leg and, in the process, she was pushing her other leg past the guard rails and out of the bed. When Nurse Kim arrived, we got Mom's legs straightened out and back in the bed where they belonged.

An hour later Dr. Meg called. Nurse Kim, David, and I were sitting at the kitchen table when the call came. Dr. Meg said that she had been looking at the X-rays and conferring with other doctors. The situation was this: Mom had the equivalent of a broken hip, a condition that was serious and painful.

We had two choices.

One was this: the hospice would approve our

putting Mom into the hospital for an operation to try to fix the broken hip. The operation might not be possible or successful. Mom might not survive the attempt. If she did, she would probably never walk again, and we might not ever be able to bring her home.

Option number two was this: keep Mom at home, give her enough morphine to mask the pain, and let nature take its course.

David, Nurse Kim, and I talked for a few minutes. But I already knew the answer. I told them, "At 92, in Mom's condition, she won't survive getting out the front door." I told Dr. Meg our decision, and she said that a nurse would be coming over immediately to show us what to do next.

When you hear the term, "let nature take its course," it sounds reassuring. Easy, even. What could be more natural than nature? But that's not how it works. Nature will take its course, all right, but it takes a lot of human intervention to make it less painful.

A hospice nurse arrived while Nurse Kim was still tending to Mom. She determined that the amount of morphine wasn't enough, and the dosage was increased. She also reviewed Mom's medications, discarding some and adding others. Together, she and Nurse Kim went over new medication instructions for me, including how to give the morphine.

I learned that most of Mom's medicines could be given to her in liquid form, and I learned how to read the measurements on a syringe. I learned that some pills could be crushed and given to Mom in applesauce. That her mouth might get dry and would need to be moistened with swabs or refrigerated and flavored "popsicles" every two hours (I could make my own, using fruit juices frozen in ice cube trays). I learned about certain ways to move people in a hospital bed, and how to change Mom's clothes and bedclothes without moving her leg too much. At first, I was terrified of moving her, but I knew, at the same time, that I needed to keep her clean because there were many accidents. But those accidents soon stopped. At the end of life, urination slows down. I learned that her eyes could become dry or irritated, so eyedrops would be needed. I learned to give Mom liquids through a straw.

It was overwhelming. I forgot half of what I was told. I had to write everything down. But the hospice nurse and Nurse Kim walked me through everything and reassured me that they would come back tomorrow. By the time that they had left for the day, Mom was asleep.

The next call was from Dr. Jan. She had been conferring with the hospice, and they had filled her in on what had happened.

This was a tough phone call for us. Dr. Jan went over Mom's condition with me and said that the hospice nurses were doing everything possible to keep Mom out of pain. And she said, as gently as she could, that she didn't think that she was needed anymore. She added, however, that she would still come if we wanted her to.

That was hard. But she was right. Dr. Jan couldn't do anything more for Mom. It was an acknowledgment that Mom had entered the last phase of her health care, and of her life.

The next morning Mom awoke, agitated again, and trying to move her leg. And she was groaning in pain, the first sign of outward pain (except for her fall) that I had seen in her in almost a year. I panicked. If you have been reading along, you will recall that I was always worried about how much things were going to cost. Well, here is the moment you have been waiting for. I didn't care how much it cost—if I had to sell the cars, the house, and the dog—I was willing to pay anything, sign anything, to stop Mom from crying out in pain. If that meant extra doctors, round-the-clock nurses, or the fanciest assisted-living facility in the state, I didn't care. I was ready to pay whatever it cost. No questions asked.

I called the hospice. I knew that they had an off-site facility and, in desperation, thought that we might be able to take Mom there *right now*. But the receptionist who answered the phone had dealt with such panic calls before. She asked me to describe Mom's condition, listened to everything I had to say, and calmed me down. She told me that she'd send a nurse out to the house right away to help. It was during this phone call that I first heard the word "transitioning," as in, "Your patient is transitioning." It means that they're dying.

The nurse who came that morning increased the dose of morphine. Mom's agitation stopped. Her pain stopped. Mom slept.

Over the next several days there was always activity around Mom—a hospice nurse, or Nurse Kim, or David, or me—coming in and out of the bedroom carrying medicine, liquids, soiled linens, you name it. There was not much activity from Mom.

One afternoon, when I had closed the bedroom door behind me, hands full of soiled bedsheets, I heard a song coming from the TV. I paused, wondering where I had heard it before. And then I realized: David was watching a re-run of *Star Trek: Voyager*. It was a television series about how Captain Kathryn Janeway and her crew made it out of the Delta Quadrant, a region full of unknowns and terrors. It had ended many years before. I had never realized how beautiful the series' theme song was. I did now. And I asked David if he could get me all the reruns to watch, and he said sure. And from that moment on, and for years afterward, I watched Captain Janeway battle her way through terrible ordeals. In every episode, some alien race would try to destroy her starship or kidnap her crew—every single week. And yet they survived, and the *Voyager* sailed on. It was comforting.

Early the next morning, about 3 a.m., Mom passed away in her sleep. It had been seven days since her fall.

It was over.

Chapter Thirteen

After the Crowd Goes Home

Death: Don't Take It Personally

I HAVE A RENEWED RESPECT FOR YOGI BERRA. He was right about a lot of things, especially when he said, "It ain't over till it's over." I could add my own epigram to that, "And you never know when it's going to be over."

During that last week of Mom's life, it occurred to me that I might be able to donate her body to science. I called a local agency that dealt with medical donations and asked them what needed to be done. They told me that there were applications to be filled out, forms to be notarized, and permissions to be approved—in short, it was a process that I should have started months ago. I was too late.

I have to tell you that a part of me was relieved. A small voice in my mind had already been whispering, "Wait a minute—you're going to let strangers do that to your mother?" My mind told me that it was the right thing to do. My emotions told me the opposite. In the end, it made no difference, since time had run out. But if it hadn't, I hope that I would have made the right decision. I'll guess I'll never know.

I have a confession to make. I don't like funerals. I know that they are important to many people, and that they can provide closure. But they're not for me. David and I decided to have Mom cremated, with just a short remembrance service at the funeral home with our minister. We had made the arrangements after Mom had fallen. The day we picked Mom's ashes up from the funeral parlor, we stopped at her favorite restaurant and bought some cream of crab soup. I think that Mom would have enjoyed the fact that her last ride had been with cream of crab, her favorite, in the back seat with her.

The question of death notices came up. Mom had not wanted us to put death notices in the newspapers when Dad had died. She figured that everyone who needed to know already did. So we didn't. But when Mom died, we put her death notice in every newspaper we could. We're glad we did. We heard from a lot of people that Mom had known, from her early days in Westport, Baltimore, and we were able to share stories. It was a good experience. Note: there's a difference between a newspaper "obituary" and a "death notice." In our area, the first is expensive, the latter, less so.

I had to do a lot of things regarding Mom's death in that first year. They ranged from changes of address to solving the mystery of what I like to call, "Mom's Golden Stock Portfolio." The latter involved quite a story. Mom's small life insurance policy had been converted to two stocks, worth $70, a long time ago. It took me an entire year to get the two stocks transferred to me because of arcane, bureaucratic rules that must have been invented in the sixteenth century. I don't think that I ever spent more time, or filled out more paperwork, to get $70 in my life.

I believe that the experts are right to advise us not to make any major decisions in the first year, if that's possible. A lot of minor, and some necessary, things have to be done anyway; why cause extra angst for yourself? Do what's necessary in that first year. Put off everything else to the next. Trust me, they will wait for you. They won't go anywhere.

And don't try to do everything all at once. No law says that you have to sort and dispose of your mom's possessions in thirty days—or else. In fact, it took me more than two years to decide what to do with all of Mom's stuff. I was glad that I didn't try to do it all immediately. Especially because, as time went by, I changed my mind about what to keep and what to give away—and what to throw away. The latter will be easier to do if you give yourself some time and space.

If you are offered grief counseling, take it. The hospice offered it to me, and while I didn't sign up for any classes, I took all the brochures and pamphlets that they had, as well as the number of someone to call if I needed help. Grief counseling reassures you that you are not alone. Other people do understand what you are going through. Seek them out. They could be in a hospice, care or prayer groups, senior centers, or in your neighborhood. But don't overdo it, either. If you join too many groups or activities right away, you may only add to your exhaustion. There is no one way to handle grief. You choose the best way for you.

No matter how prepared you are, death is a shock. It's a strange thing to contemplate, but in my mom's case, although she had been ill for a long time, her death came suddenly. Be easy on yourself. Don't expect life to get back to normal one day later. Take care of yourself physically as well as emotionally. Your body may respond by getting sick itself (I'm told that this is fairly common). Drink lots of water and get plenty of sleep. Go to your doctor if you feel ill, and make sure to tell your doctor about the recent death in your family. That information will help them. They can take better care of you if they know the stress that you have been under.

You probably had a lot of things that you liked to do before your mom became ill. Revisit them. Pick one or two and start up again. But, again, don't overdo it.

Also, be aware that some weird things may happen to you. They happened to me. It's not uncommon to think that you see or hear the deceased wandering around. It's okay. You're not going crazy. It's just your mind, working in overdrive, trying to make sense of what's happened.

There were also some coincidences that made me smile, then and now. The year before Mom died, a stray cat who had wandered into our yard around Halloween took up residence with us for a while. We named him Edgar. We arranged for him to be adopted right after Mom died (keeping him was not an option, since Edgar and Clara were not destined to become best friends). About a week later, after Mom had died, when I was in the grocery store parking lot, I saw a cat just like Edgar sitting on the top of a car, and he was staring right at me. Was that Edgar? Or was that Mom, disguised as Edgar?

And I won't forget the red fox episode. A few days before Mom passed away, we saw a red fox run across our backyard. We hadn't seen a fox in our yard for many, many years. My dad used to be a foxhunter. When David saw the fox, he said, "That must be your dad, looking for your mom."

On the day that Mom died, Clara stopped jumping up onto the sofa and chairs to sit with us. Those were the places where she liked to nap. It was about a week later before she returned to her normal activities. Had she been upset that Mom was now gone?

Anyway, the point of these stories is just to let you know that your mind may be more active than usual, and you may pick up on things you normally wouldn't be aware of. It's all okay.

Perhaps now is the time to start thinking about your own future. You've read about what happened with Mom. Is that how you want to arrange things? Or would a different path be better for you? You don't have to make any final decisions now. It's also a good time to think about any changes that you might need to make to your will or to your own health directives. Your lawyer can advise you.

The next chapter consists of a list of the things that I needed to do after Mom's death. I know—another list! But it's not long, and not all of it may apply to you. It can, however, serve as a handy guide for things that you may need to do. You can check them off as you complete each one. (Yes, go ahead and write in this book—it's yours, you know!)

Chapter Fourteen

Checklist for Afterwards

- Get more death certificates from the funeral home than you think you'll need (ten is enough if your mom was not financially active; more may be needed if she was).

- Make sure that the funeral home will notify Social Security and other relevant organizations.

- Make sure that the life insurance company is informed.

- Call your lawyer; she will know what to do about the will.

- Estates: even if you think that everything is in your name, open a small estate (your lawyer will help you). That way, if something has slipped through the cracks, you will be covered (this was a lesson learned from my adventure in the wilds of the stock market world).

- Return medical equipment (personal alarm system, handicapped parking space card, etc.)

- Dispose of medicines (ask the hospice nurse for advice).

- Dispose of medical supplies (Goodwill, Salvation Army, etc.).

- Ensure that the bank accounts are up to date. You may not want to take your mom's name off the bank account just yet. Sometimes, later on, you may get deposits with your mom's name on them, and it's easier to deposit them if her name is still on the account.

- Get your mom's medical records from doctors. You never know if you will need them (or, if your relatives might need them one day).

- Check that you are receiving and paying all the necessary bills.

- Fill out change of address forms that you need to for any bills that need paying. I believe that it's wise not to take your mom's name off the bills until at least six months have passed.

- If a religious or social group has assisted with the funeral, make a donation.

- Thank everyone who sent flowers, made calls, etc.

- Regarding family files, photographs, diaries, precious mementos, etc.: for now, just sort everything by category and store them where you can easily find them later on. They will all be waiting for you when you are ready to go through them.

See? Isn't that enough to keep you busy
for one year?

EPILOGUE

I GUESS THAT'S IT. As I write this, it's been more than two years since Mom passed away. I think that I covered most of the important events. If I left anything out, I apologize. You can let me know. Drop me at line on my website: www.threevillagesmedia. wordpress.com.

My hope is that something I've said in this book will help you. If just one of you—hey, I see you!—raises their hand in the affirmative, writing this book will have been worth it.

I have wondered, and worried, a little, about what Mom would have thought about this book, which, of necessity, reveals personal information about her. Mom was a private person. In ordinary times, she would not have dreamed of telling strangers her personal problems. But in this case, I think it's all right. Mom would want to help others with dementia to have a better life than she had. And if I'm wrong about this, Mom will probably let me know, sometime, somewhere, somehow (uh-oh!).

You may have wondered about all the quotes; especially the Shakespeare ones. I like Shakespeare. He knew about life. And death. If you want to read the work of someone who really understands what you are going through, Shakespeare is your man. Many thanks to Cynthia Barry, educator, for introducing me to Henry and his friends.

I want to thank my husband, David, for his love, help, and guidance during not only the years of Mom's illness, but also during the writing of this book. He is the best.

Thanks to my brother-in-law, Scott; my niece, Nicole; and my nephew, Rory, for their understanding and help.

Thanks, also, to all the people at Capital Coordinated Medicine, the Hospice of the Chesapeake, the O'Malley Senior Center, and the Anne Arundel County Department of Aging. Thanks to Dr. Jan, Dr. Meg, Nurse Kim, Nurse Therese (Trez) Trainum, and the hospice nurse who braved the storm to come help us. Thanks to Dr. D.,

Carol, Trisha, Monika, and Sherry. Thank you, also, to the wonderful people who helped build the addition to the house, and to our friends and neighbors who supported us in so many ways.

Thanks to everyone else who helped us out but whom I didn't mention here . . . thank you.

A special shout-out goes to *Star Trek: Voyager*. Seriously, watch one of those re-runs, and listen to that theme song. It's inspirational.

Thank you, the reader, for taking this journey back in time with me.

And finally, to quote Mom: *just sing.*

ABOUT THE AUTHOR

LEONA ILLIG is a fiction and nonfiction writer who lives in Maryland with her husband, David, and a small spaniel named Clara.

Her fiction includes a children's

Author photograph by David Illig

book, *The Elephant and the Bird Feeder*, and a coming-of-age novella, *Thumper: Life on the Farm*. Her short stories have been published by *The MacGuffin* and others. Her humorous nonfiction articles have been published by the Astronomical Society of the Pacific and by *Sky & Telescope*, the premier astronomy magazine in the United States. Her books, articles, and stories appear under the bylines L. Upton Illig and Leona Illig.

She holds an associate's degree in elementary education from Anne Arundel Community College and a master's degree in English literature from the University of Maryland, College Park. She is a member of the Maryland Writers' Association, the Eastern Shore Writers' Association, and others.

For more information, please visit her website at www.threevillagesmedia.wordpress.com